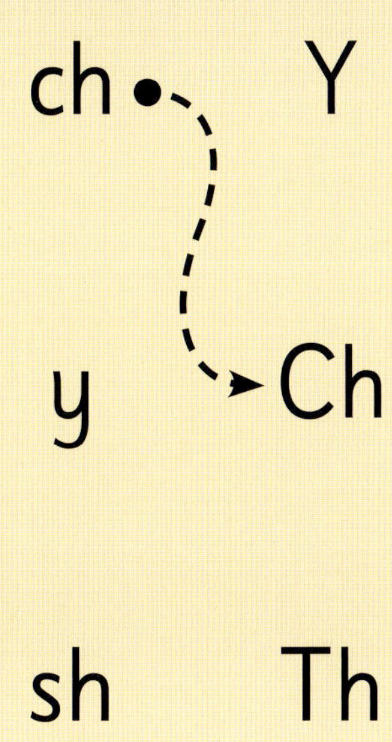

th X

x Sh

Dad and Max need three eggs and six mushrooms.

- □ a big pan
- □ a wooden spoon
- □ a balloon whisk
- □ six mushrooms
- □ six fresh eggs in a box

Dad chops mushrooms. Chop, chop, chop!

Max gets three eggs...

...then cracks them.

Smash! Max drops an egg!

- froth
- eggshell

Dad whisks eggs.

Dad and Max mix eggs and mushrooms.

Is it cooked yet?
Yes!

Max and Dad have omelet with corn and rocket for lunch.

munch
Yum!
crunch

Yum or yuck?

☺☹ mushrooms

☺☹ rocket

☺☹ corn

☺☹ eggs

☺☹ omelet